# The VEGETABLE Lover

## COLORING BOOK

instagram: @jenracinecoloring

facebook.com/jenracinecoloring

www.jenracine.com

**Jen Racine COLORING BOOKS**

## FIND ALL JEN RACINE BOOKS AT ON-LINE BOOKSELLERS

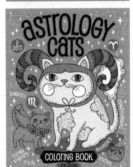

## COLORING PAGES AVAILABLE IN ETSY SHOP:

### WWW.ETSY.COM/SHOP/JENRACINECOLORING

# ABOUT THIS BOOK

*This coloring book is intended as a useful and enjoyable introduction to popular vegetables along with their lesser known varieties. Vegetables can come in a dazzling array of colors which make them beautiful subjects to embellish and enjoy!*

**30** ILLUSTRATIONS OF BEAUTIFUL VEGETABLES ARE LABELED WITH THEIR NAMES ALONG WITH INTERESTING FACTS SUCH AS WHERE THEY ORIGINATE, PEAK SEASON, OR SUGGESTIONS FOR COOKING.

 *Where from?*

 *Peak season*

 *Fun facts*

 *Cooking suggestions*

**COLOR** *A great way to help you color this book is to look up images on the internet as a guide. A simple search using "images" will give you ideas for coloring each bean or ear of corn accurately.*

**NOTE:** THE PAPER IN THIS BOOK IS BEST SUITED FOR COLORED PENCILS, MILDLINERS OR CRAYONS. WET MEDIA SUCH AS HEAVILY SATURATED MARKERS OR WATERCOLORS DO NOT HOLD UP WELL.

**VEGETABLES** *are delicious, nutritious and fun to grow and eat! Even better, they come in a wide variety of colors and shapes. This coloring book is a small sample of the different kinds of vegetables available and not a comprehensive guide. My hope is that you will find enjoyment and information in these pages and that you will want to seek out varieties that you have not yet tried. Eat the rainbow, support your local farmers or grow yourself!*

# HAPPY COLORING, VEGETABLE LOVERS!

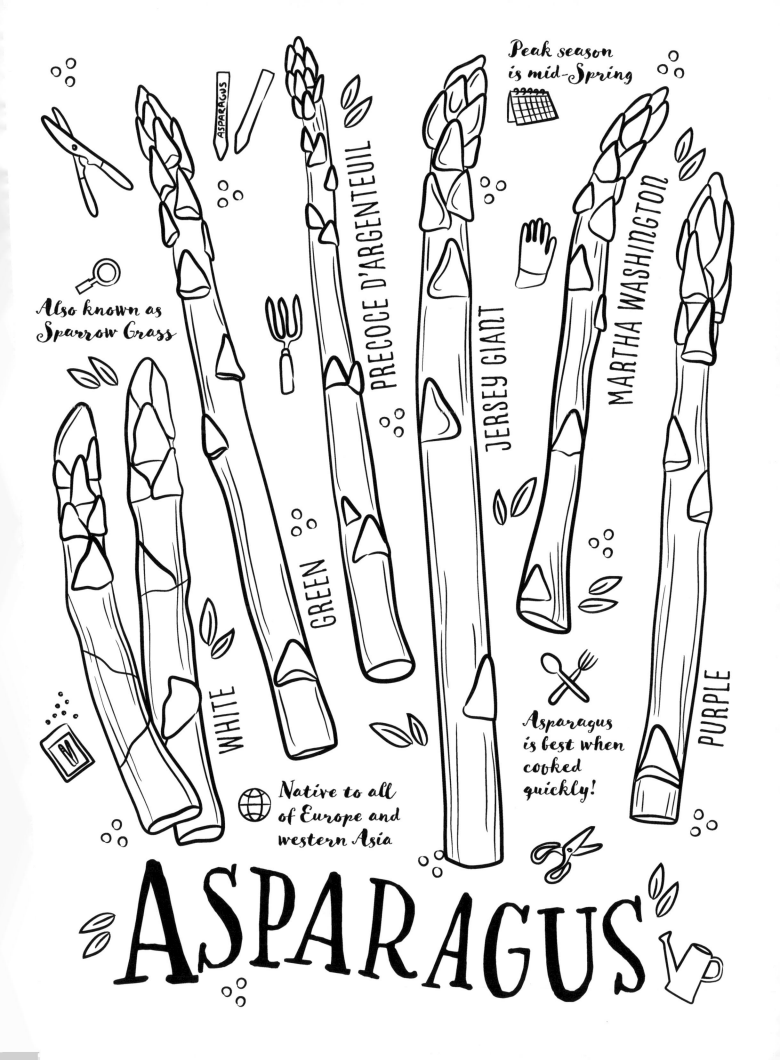

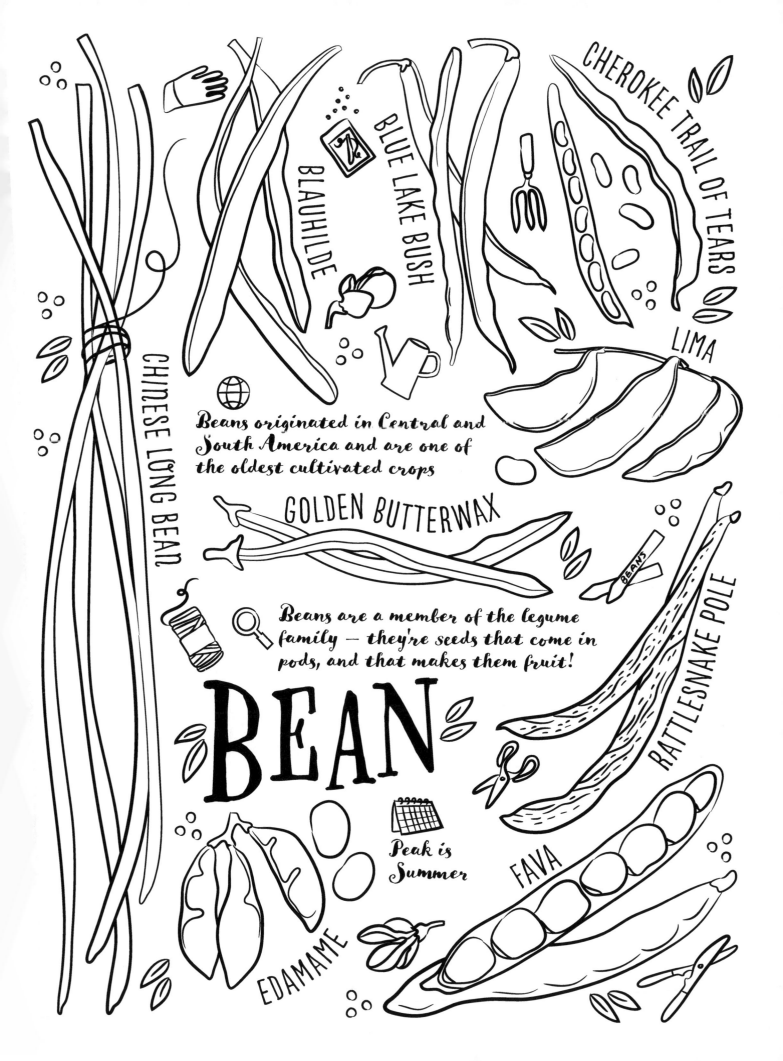

BLAUHILDE

BLUE LAKE BUSH

CHEROKEE TRAIL OF TEARS

LIMA

CHINESE LONG BEAN

Beans originated in Central and South America and are one of the oldest cultivated crops

GOLDEN BUTTERWAX

Beans are a member of the legume family — they're seeds that come in pods, and that makes them fruit!

BEAN

RATTLESNAKE POLE

Peak is Summer

FAVA

EDAMAME

CYLINDRA

DETROIT DARK RED

GOLDEN

BEET

Beets originated in the ancient Middle East and were grown primarily for their greens by ancient Egyptians, Greeks and Romans

CHIOGGIA

Harvested in summer – available all year

Referred to as Beetroot in British English

ALBINO

EGYPTIAN

BULL'S BLOOD

Buy beets with the leaves attached – cut off 2 inches from top at home for best storage

Beet leaf

# BOK CHOY

Winter months are peak season

MILK

BABY

Means "white vegetable" in Cantonese — also known as Pak Choi, Bok Choi, and Pak Choy

Eat raw or cooked. Stir fry over high heat until tender-crisp!

GREEN

A type of Chinese cabbage

PURPLE LADY

Bok Choy is native to China, specifically the Yangtze River Delta area, one of the oldest agricultural regions in the world

TATSOI — similar to Bok Choy but native to Japan

BROCCOLI RAAB OR RAPINI

Romanesco is sometimes considered a Cauliflower but flavor is more similar to Broccoli

Native to the eastern Mediterranean and Asia

ROMANESCO

CALABRESE

CHINESE

Peak season is Fall through Spring

BROCCOLI

Broccoli leaf

Broccolini is a hybrid of Calabrese and Chinese!

BROCCOLINI

Belongs to the Cabbage family

PURPLE SPROUTING

BROCCOLI

# BRUSSELS SPROUT

Peak season is late Fall and Winter

RED RUBINE

BRUSSEL SPROUT

GREEN

Belongs to the Cabbage family

Brussels Sprout leaf

Try roasted Brussels Sprouts!

First appeared in northern Europe during the 5th century, later being cultivated in the 13th century near Brussels, Belgium, from which they derived their name

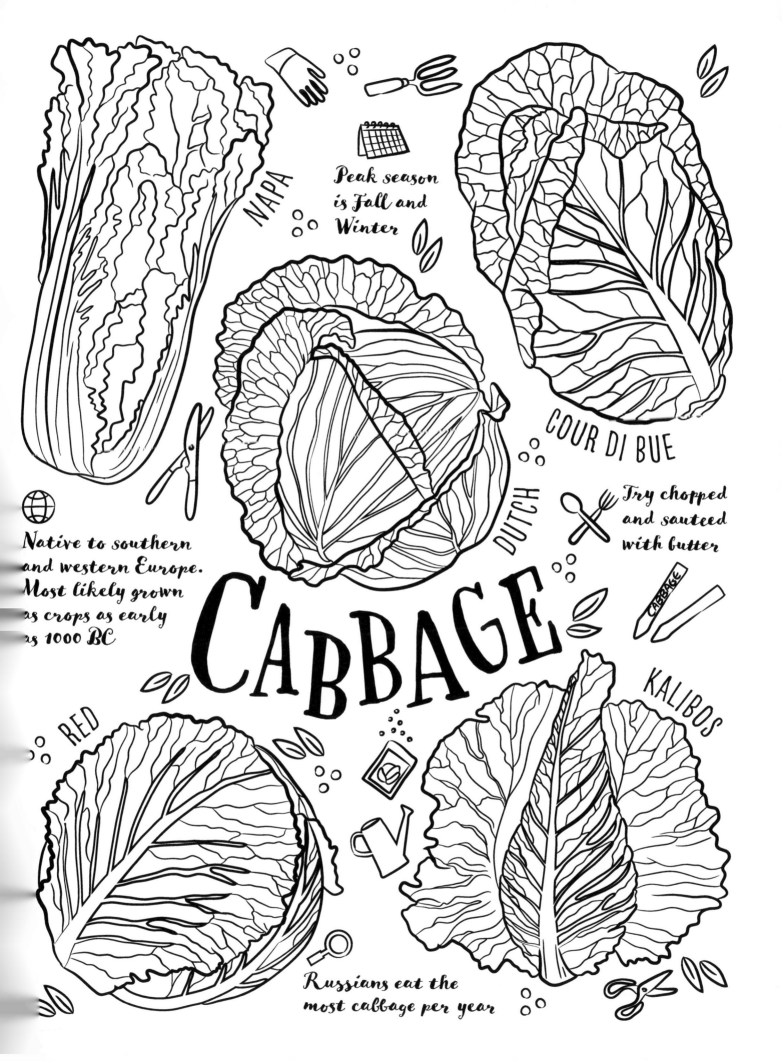

NAPA

Peak season is Fall and Winter

COUR DI BUE

DUTCH

Try chopped and sauteed with butter

CABBAGE

CABBAGE

Native to southern and western Europe. Most likely grown as crops as early as 1000 BC

KALIBOS

RED

Russians eat the most cabbage per year

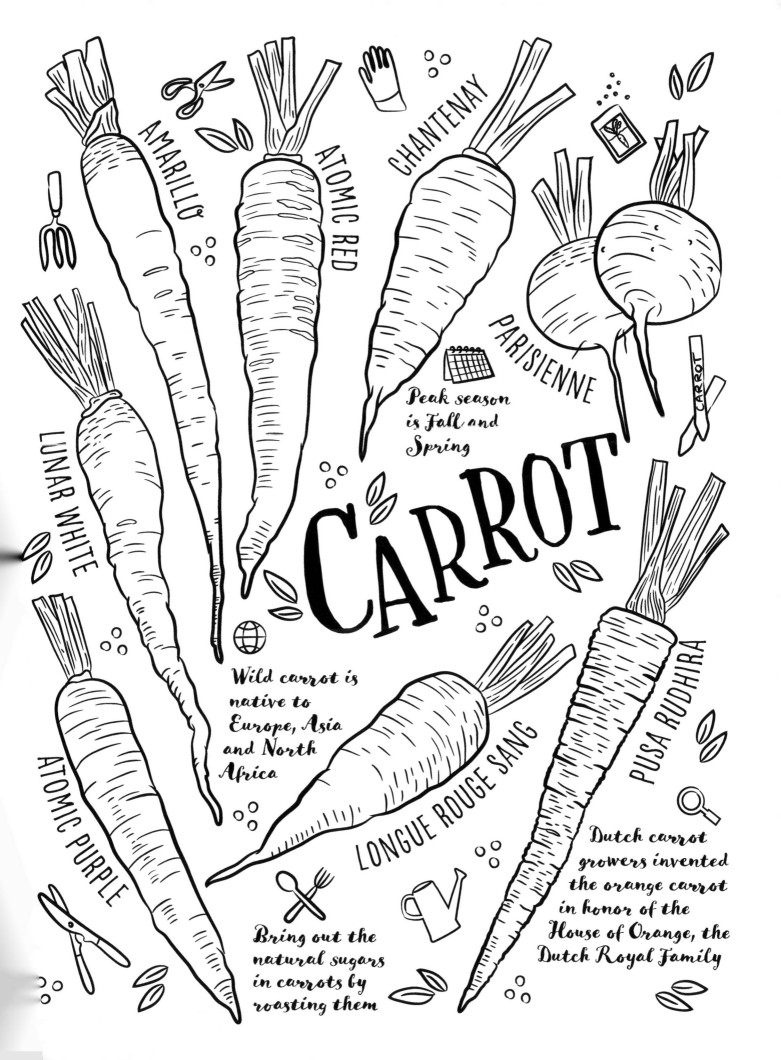

CARROT

AMARILLO

ATOMIC RED

CHANTENAY

PARISIENNE

LUNAR WHITE

ATOMIC PURPLE

LONGUE ROUGE SANG

PUSA RUDHIRA

Peak season is Fall and Spring

Wild carrot is native to Europe, Asia and North Africa

Bring out the natural sugars in carrots by roasting them

Dutch carrot growers invented the orange carrot in honor of the House of Orange, the Dutch Royal Family

# CAULIFLOWER

Cauliflower is native to Asia and Northeastern Mediterranean

Peak season is early Fall

WHITE

CHEDDAR

PURPLE

CAULIFLOWER

Try roasting with olive oil and herbs

GREEN

The word cauliflower derives from the Italian cavolfiore, meaning cabbage flower

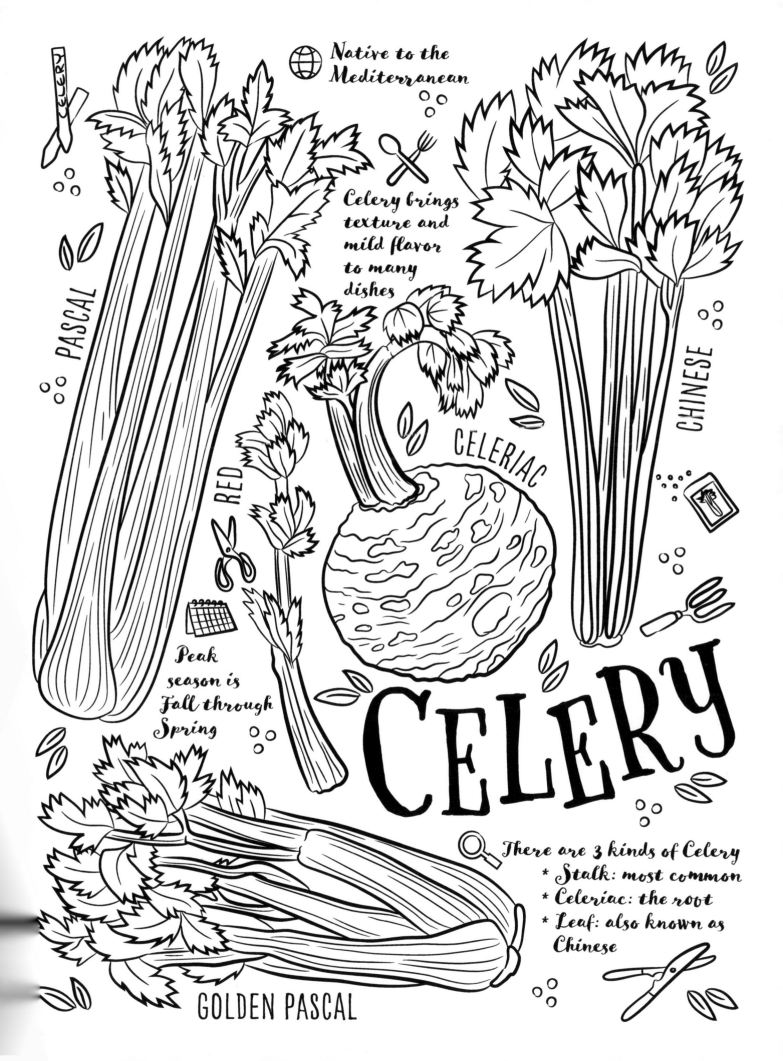

Native to the Mediterranean

Celery brings texture and mild flavor to many dishes

PASCAL

RED

CELERIAC

CHINESE

Peak season is Fall through Spring

# CELERY

There are 3 kinds of Celery
* Stalk: most common
* Celeriac: the root
* Leaf: also known as Chinese

GOLDEN PASCAL

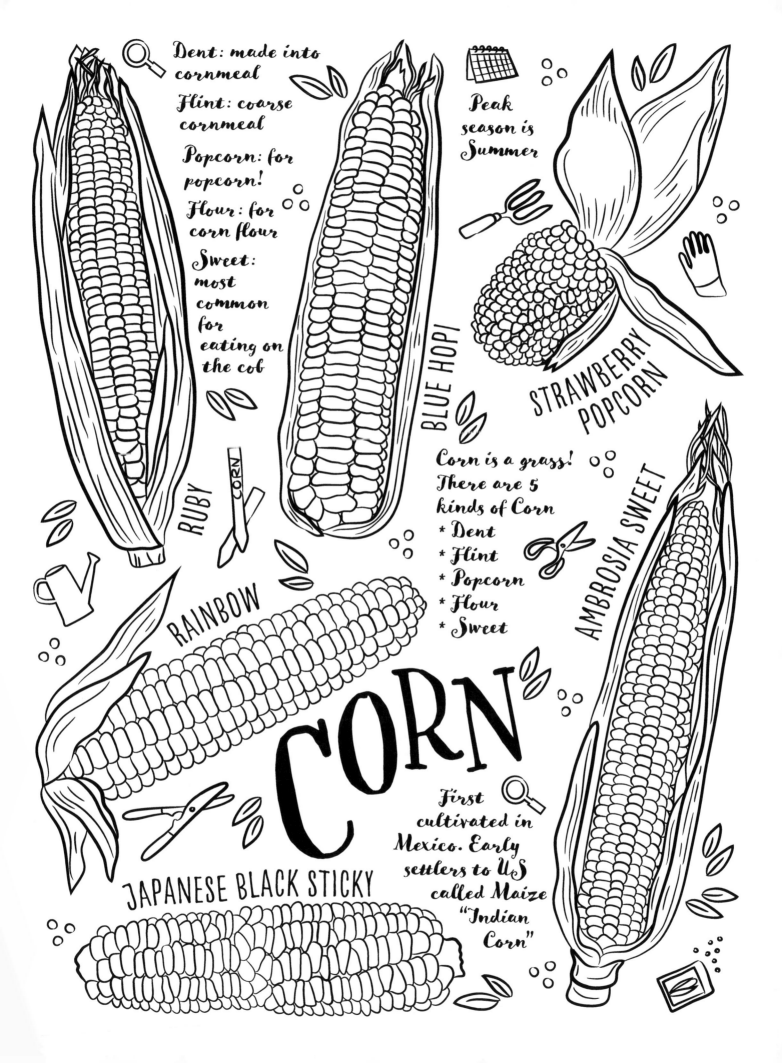

# CORN

Dent: made into cornmeal

Flint: coarse cornmeal

Popcorn: for popcorn!

Flour: for corn flour

Sweet: most common for eating on the cob

Peak season is Summer

STRAWBERRY POPCORN

BLUE HOPI

RUBY

Corn is a grass! There are 5 kinds of Corn
* Dent
* Flint
* Popcorn
* Flour
* Sweet

AMBROSIA SWEET

RAINBOW

JAPANESE BLACK STICKY

First cultivated in Mexico. Early settlers to US called Maize "Indian Corn"

# CUCUMBER

Native to India and introduced to Europe by the Romans

ARMENIAN

KYURI

Cucumbers have flowers and seeds so botanically, they are fruit!

ENGLISH

GHERKIN

CUCUMBER

PERSIAN

Peak season Spring and Summer

LEMON

GARDEN

PICKLING

Fresh is best!

GRAFFITI

JAPANESE

ITALIAN

INDIAN

THAI

Peak season is Summer

Also known as Aubergine or Brinjal – botanically Eggplant is a berry!

WHITE

GLOBE

EGGPLANT

ROSA BIANCA

Delicious baked, mashed, fried or roasted

EGGPLANT

FAIRY TALE

Native to India

REDBOR

Native to eastern Mediterranean and Asia

RUSSIAN

Try chopped and rubbed with salt

LACINATO

CHINESE

CURLY

Peak season is Fall and Winter

# KALE

Kale originates from Northern Middle English word "Cale"

PORTUGUESE

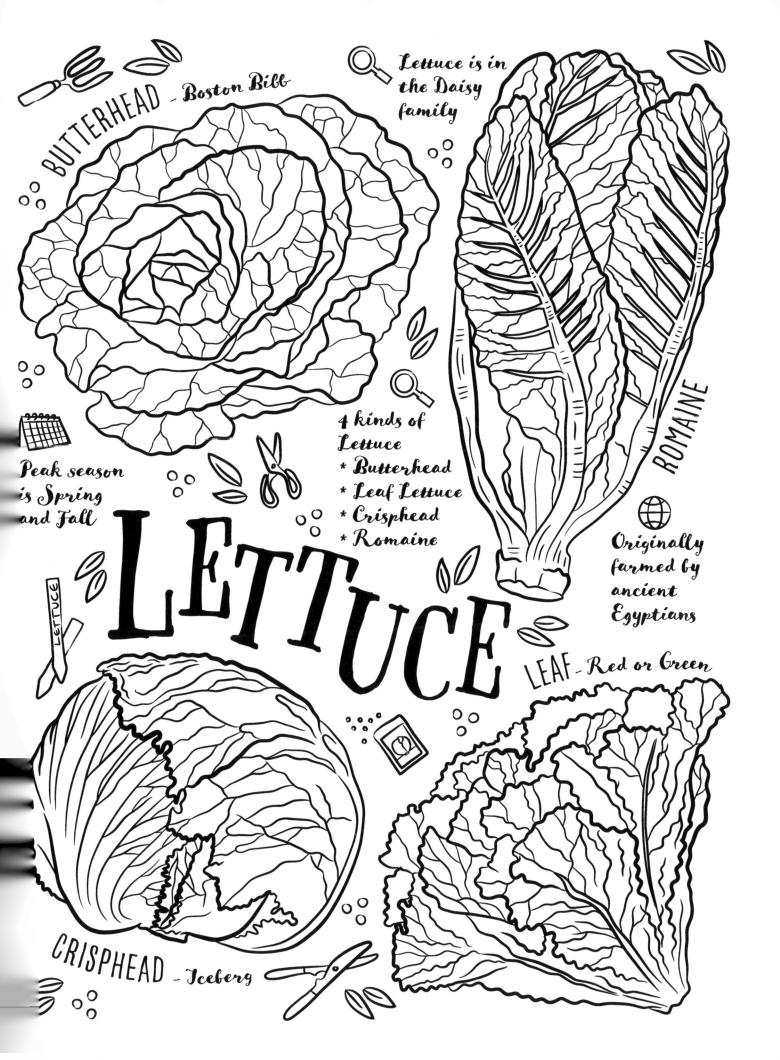

BUTTERHEAD - Boston Bibb

Lettuce is in the Daisy family

Peak season is Spring and Fall

LETTUCE

Lettuce

4 kinds of Lettuce
* Butterhead
* Leaf Lettuce
* Crisphead
* Romaine

ROMAINE

Originally farmed by ancient Egyptians

LEAF - Red or Green

CRISPHEAD - Iceberg

Peak season is Summer

HONEYDEW

PEPINO

MELON

Native to central Asia

CASABA

CHARENTAIS

Melons have a central seed cavity

KOREAN

MELON

CANTELOPE

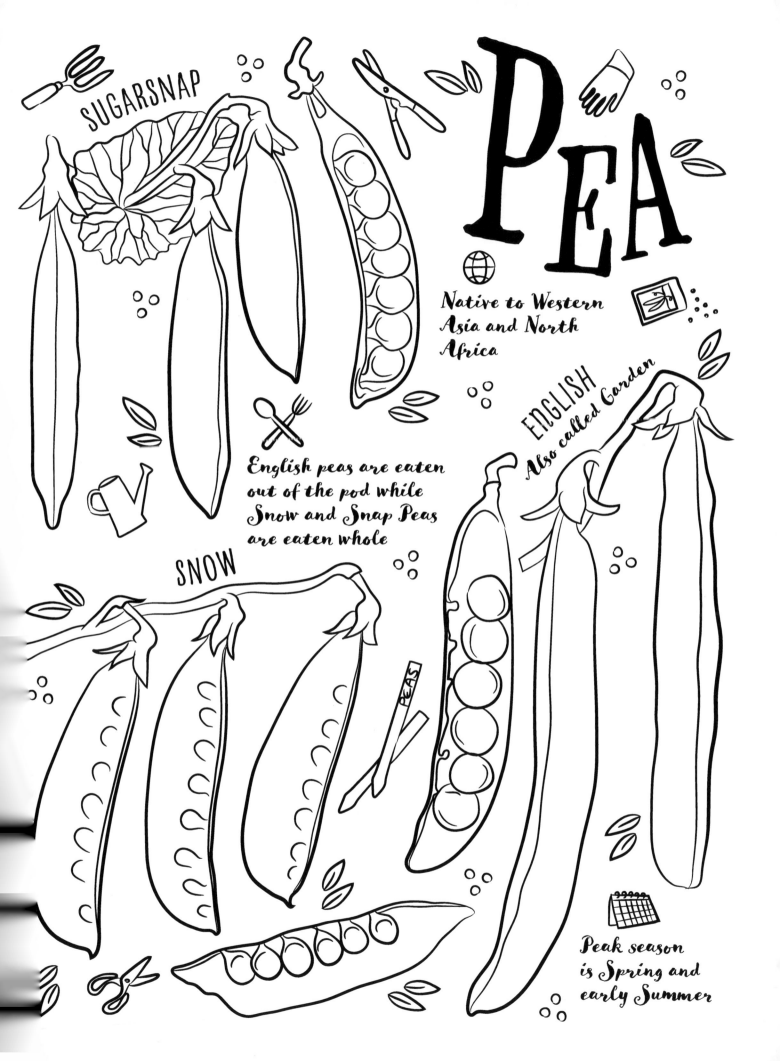

# PEA

SUGARSNAP

Native to Western Asia and North Africa

English peas are eaten out of the pod while Snow and Snap Peas are eaten whole

SNOW

ENGLISH
Also called Garden

PEAS

Peak season is Spring and early Summer

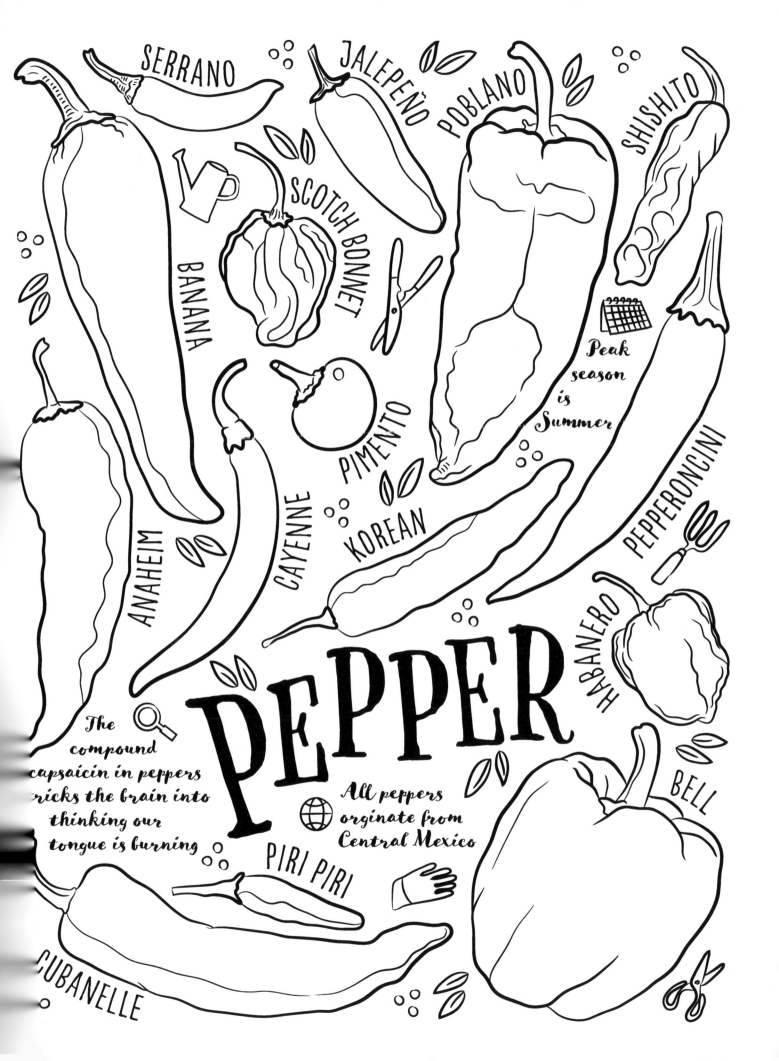

SERRANO

JALEPEÑO

POBLANO

SHISHITO

SCOTCH BONNET

BANANA

PIMENTO

Peak season is Summer

ANAHEIM

CAYENNE

KOREAN

PEPPERONCINI

HABANERO

PEPPER

The compound capsaicin in peppers tricks the brain into thinking our tongue is burning

All peppers orginate from Central Mexico

BELL

PIRI PIRI

CUBANELLE

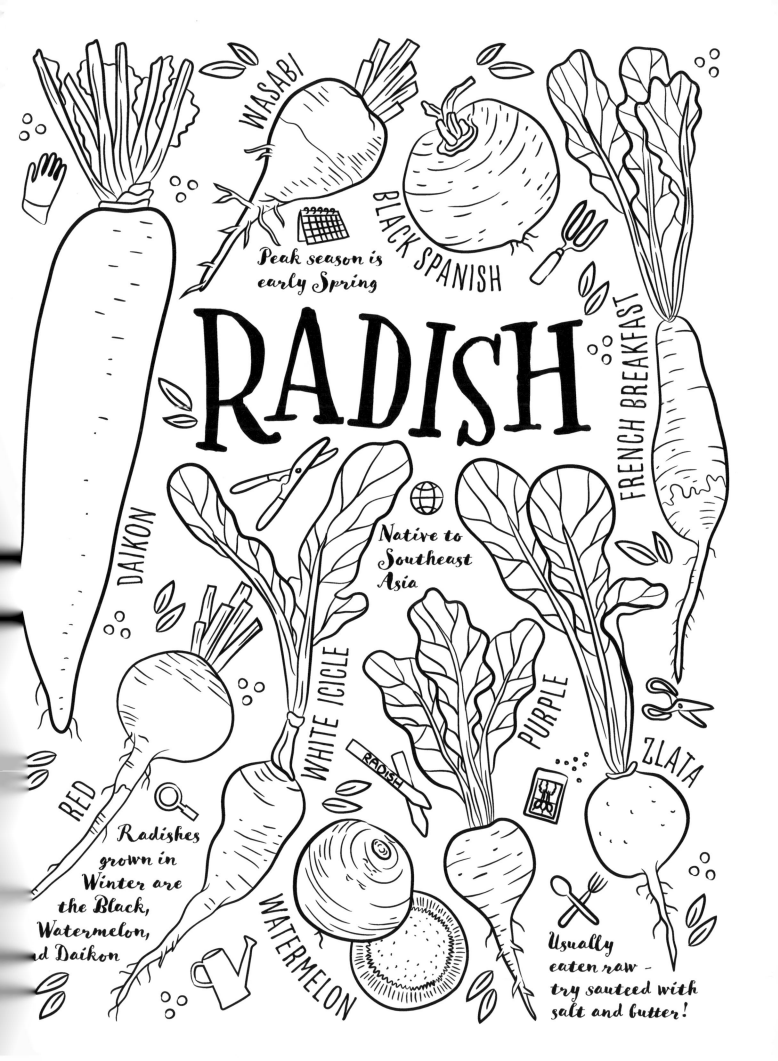

WASABI

BLACK SPANISH

FRENCH BREAKFAST

Peak season is early Spring

# RADISH

Native to Southeast Asia

DAIKON

WHITE ICICLE

PURPLE

ZLATA

RADISH

RED

Radishes grown in Winter are the Black, Watermelon, d Daikon

WATERMELON

Usually eaten raw - try sauteed with salt and butter!

BLOOMSDALE

AMSTERDAM
PRICKLY SEEDED

GIANT NOBLE

SPINACH

First
cultivated
in Persia

CHINESE MULTI-COLOR

BABY

SPACE

SPINACH

RED MALABAR

Peak season
is Spring
and Fall

Spinach has
3 categories:
1. Flat leaf
2. Savoy - curly leaves
3. Semi-savoy

# SUMMER SQUASH

CHAYOTE

ROUND ZUCCHINI

ZUCCHINI

CROOKNECK

ZEPHYR

LEMON

TATUMA

Summer is peak season

PATTYPAN

SQUASH

Summer squash are squashes that are harvested young while the rind is still tender

Native to the Americas

GOLDEN ZUCCHINI

COUSA

TROMBONCINO

BARESE

Peak season is early Spring and Fall but can last through Summer

RAINBOW

ORANGE FANTASIA

WHITE RIBBED

Sauté with garlic and onion

The origin of the adjective "Swiss" is unclear, since this coastal plant is not native to Switzerland

# SWISS CHARD

SWISS CHARD

Native to southern Europe and much older than the related Beet

MAGENTA SUNSET

# TOMATO

ROMA

CHERRY

Originated in Western South America

RED BEEFSTEAK

PINK BRANDYWINE

BLACK KRIM

SUNGOLD

GREEN ZEBRA

Botanically, tomatoes are fruit

CHEROKEE PURPLE

Peak season is Summer

PEAR

GOLDEN JUBILEE

SAN MARZANO

TOMATO

Made in the USA
Las Vegas, NV
21 January 2024

84700472R00037